What About Me?

Written and Illustrated by

Bridget Smith

To order additional copies of this book, visit
bridgetbuildscharacter.com

DEDICATION

To my children, Jonathan, Blake, and
Emilee, who possess talents the amaze
and fill our lives with fun, laugher and
joy. God has blessed my family beyond
measure!

ACKNOWLEDGEMENTS

First of all I want to thank God for everything that I do! He is my why, my how, my when, my what, my who—my everything!
I want to thank my friend Mary Grice for helping to edit my story, my niece Nena Hutcherson for the last-minute changes, My Daughter Emilee and son-in-law Stephen Hunt for helping with the color scheme and adjustments, my sister Lisa Lew, friends Laurie Alabach and Ashley Bryan for the input on the artwork, son Blake Smith, sister Jodi Jones, sister-in-law Mary Barnes, and friend Carmen Freeman for always listening to all my ideas.

Special thanks to Kristen Henderson for making my book my own

ALSO INCLUDED:

Glossary

Comprehensive Questions

Song "I Want to Be Somebody" music composed/lyrics written by Bridget Smith

Illustrations/literature/music

Bridget Smith

SUMMARY:

In this beautifully illustrated picture book, titled "What About Me?" a grasshopper overcomes insecurity by discovering his great music ability. Then he realizes that everyone around him has a special talent. What really makes Chopper special?

Summer was at its end and the hot summer sun beamed down on Carmella as she dug into the soft brown dirt. Carmella was a graceful emerald-green grasshopper. She had always cherished life and savored each moment. She knew in her heart this was the day she had been waiting for.

Knowing it was her destiny, she relentlessly deposited her densely bound cluster of delicate pale orange eggs into the safety of the soil. After she had finished, she felt the uncertainty in her heart of what her nymphs' future would be.

Winter came and gradually passed. Soft white snow melted, and small blades of Bahia grass began popping through the soil. As the seasons changed, the weather grew warmer.

One curious little grasshopper nymph, which is a young grasshopper, began to hurriedly dig his way to the top. Being the lead nymph, he knew all the other nymphs would soon follow.

As he glanced around for the first time, he noticed all the nymphs looked alike. There were so many of them!

He then found his mother, Carmella. She looked beautiful to him. She looked lovingly down into his deep brown eyes and declared his name to be Chopper. Chopper loved his mother, and she adored him. She showed her love equally to each of her offspring.

Although Chopper's childhood
was wonderful, he had always
felt insignificant.

Carmella explained to him how all grasshoppers go through incomplete metamorphosis; in each stage, the grasshopper grows larger without changing in its appearance. The only change the grasshopper goes through is growing wings as an adult. This realization made Chopper even sadder. He had always wanted to be special. Chopper began to wonder how he could ever be "somebody" when he was just like everyone else.

Every night, in the midst of the plush velvety green meadows, the locals joined each other to make music. Chopper never missed an evening. Elder male grasshoppers gathered in a group as the mothers and their nymphs sat around them. They enjoyed listening to music while gazing at the stars that sparkled like diamonds. Families and loners alike looked forward to their evening serenade. No one grasshopper ever knew who was going to lead or what songs would be made. This was a true celebration of life, and Chopper loved every moment. Each grasshopper made a different sound. Joined together, their sounds made a sweet melody.

As the music began to fade, the grasshoppers fell into a peaceful sleep. It was a wonderful way to end the day.

One bright sunny afternoon, Chopper was jumping around watching other grasshoppers play.

Still wishing to be unique, Chopper settled softly onto a wide green blade of Bahia grass and began playing enchanting chords; it sounded like angels singing. Whenever grasshoppers rub their back legs with their forewings, like someone strumming their fingers on a harp, they produce a spectacular sound. This process is called stridulating. During this time Chopper felt peaceful and happy. Music seemed to lift his spirits.

On this particular day, he discovered a slightly different tune. He was astonished at his newfound ability. It was the most wonderful sound he had ever heard, and it came from him. Other grasshoppers heard it, too, and began to gather around him. Grasshoppers throughout the land came to hear Chopper.   As he played, he realized how extraordinary his music was. That's when he finally knew what made him special.

As time went on, he began to listen to other grasshoppers play their individual songs. He realized that if everyone else joined with him, adding their music to his, their new melodies would be like a grand symphony. He appreciated that everyone was unique and relished the idea that together they would make the most magnificent music in the land.

Chopper then realized that not only was he special, but so was everyone else in his or her own way.

I Want To Be Somebody

Bridget Smith

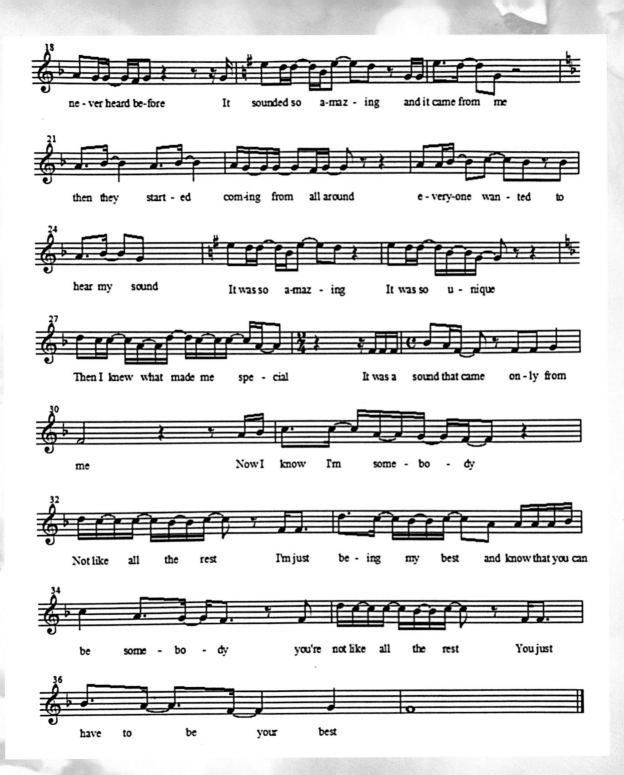

GLOSSARY

BEAMED – to shine brightly

CHERISHED – to value with great love and care

SAVORED – enjoyed

DESTINY – that which has happened or must happen to someone because of fate

RELENTLESSLY – without stopping or slackening; persistent

DENSELY – having parts very close together with little space between

BOUND – the area within or limit of something; border

CLUSTER – a small, close group of things that are alike.

DELICATE – easy to break or hurt

UNCERTAINTY – that which is unknown, indefinite, or changeable

NYMPH – an insect in an early stage of life. A nymph looks like a small adult.

INCOMPLETE METAMORPHOSIS – insect development, as in the grasshopper and cricket, in which the change is gradual with the absence of a pupal stage.

COMPREHENSIVE QUESTIONS

1. Which season do grasshoppers lay eggs? Winter, Summer, Spring or Fall (answer: Summer)

2. What color were the grasshopper's eggs? (answer: pale orange)

3. Which season do the grasshoppers come out of the ground? Winter, Summer, Spring, or Fall (answer: Spring)

4. What is the only change that grasshoppers have in incomplete metamorphosis? (answer: they grow wings)

5. Why was Carmella feeling unsure about the future of her offspring? (She didn't know if they would be safe, happy, successful, etc.)

MORE COMPREHENSIVE QUESTIONS

6. If you were Carmella, would you be worried about your offspring?

7. Why did Chopper not feel special? (possible answer: Chopper felt like he was just like everyone else.)

8. What happened to Chopper to make him feel like he was somebody important? (answer: He discovered his ability to play beautiful music.)

9. What made Chopper confident? (He overcame his insecurity by realizing his ability to play beautiful music.)

10. Why do you think that after Chopper felt confident, he noticed how well the others played?

11. Do you think that it is important to see value in yourself and others? If so, why?

Check out more books in the

CONCEPT AND CHARACTER SERIES

Chloe's Destiny

If I could count to ten...

more books coming soon!

Made in the USA
Middletown, DE
03 February 2022

60373224R00024